ABOUT VALERIE

Chalkboard artist and hand letterer Valerie McKeehan has been drawing and illustrating since childhood. A lifelong creative, her passion for commercial art began simply and without pretense: producing hand-lettered signs for her father's business. In 2012, newly wedded and drawing from a love of visual storytelling honed through her career in advertising, Valerie transformed an old picture frame into a "McKeehan's Café" chalkboard for the kitchen. She instantly fell in love with chalkboard art.

Drawn to the simplicity of chalk and the nostalgia that it inspires, Valerie opened her online chalkboard boutique, Lily and Val, in 2012. Whimsical and undeniably handcrafted, her designs are honest and authentic, at home with their imperfections and unique character. Working out of her home studio in Pittsburgh, Pennsylvania at a desk constructed by her husband, she lovingly creates each piece entirely by hand, from sketch to slate, illustrating inspirational quotations or simply depicting everyday subjects that inspire her work, such as coffee and cooking.

It's the spontaneity of life's playful, everyday pleasures that inspires Valerie. The smallest things are the most important things: a few words transforming a room into a cozy space, an illustration that makes you smile. Valerie revels in mixing simple nostalgia with a modern style of pretty-whimsy to create beautiful designs that are lovingly made.

Valerie's work has been featured in many publications, media outlets, and noteworthy blogs, including: The Food Network, *Martha Stewart Living Magazine, The Knot Magazine, Good Housekeeping Magazine, HGTV.com, Huffington Post, Real Simple.com, Flea Market Style Magazine, Smart Magazine, Country Living.com, BuzzFeed, Life & Style Weekly.com,* and *Style Me Pretty.*

She is the author of the books *The Complete Book of Chalk Lettering: Create & Develop Your Own Style, Chalk-Style Botanicals Deluxe Coloring Book, Chalk-Style Expressions Coloring Book,* and *Chalk-Style Celebrations Coloring Book.*

CREATIVE PROCESS: HOW CHALK ART BECOMES A PERMANENT DESIGN

Each piece I create starts out as a hand-lettered and illustrated design. Most of my designs begin as a pencil sketch. When I'm sketching, I usually have a quote in mind or something that I have to get out on the page. I use the sketch to help determine the layout of the finished piece and the font styles I would like to use. I change my mind lots of times and keep making adjustments until I'm happy with the design.

When the design is ready, I take it to one of my chalkboards. When I reach this stage, I work in layers, starting with a rough sketch first. Then I go back and refine the design by adding details, sharpening the letters, creating shading—all of the things that will make the piece really pop and give it a finished look.

When I've finished my chalkboard design, I take a photograph of it and import it to my computer as a digital image. There is something so real and authentic about hand-drawn, hand-lettered art, but by bringing the art onto the computer, I can share it with you!

When I'm happy with my pencil sketch, I draw the design on one of my chalkboards and refine it by adding detail and shading.

Almost every design starts as a rough pencil sketch where I make decisions about the layout and font style I will use.

When the chalkboard design is finished, I take a photograph of it and import it to my computer where I can make further revisions if I want to, like adding color.

HERE ARE SOME MORE
EXAMPLES OF CHALKBOARD
ART THAT I HAVE CREATED!

HOLIDAY WASSAIL

4 CUPS APPLE CIDER

4 CUPS ORANGE JUICE

4 CUPS cranberry juice

1/3 CUP BROWN SUGAR

1 ORANGE (SLICED)

1 LEMON (SLICED)

Combine all ingredients in a slow cooker and cook on low

6-8 HOURS

serve warm

3 CINNAMON sticks

2 in. fresh GINGER SLICED

2 tsp WHOLE CLOVES

A DONUT is HAPPINESS WITH sprinkles ON TOP

the only way to find yourself is to get lost

Warm AND FUZZY

HOLIDAY WISHES

COLOR THEORY

Picking the colors you want to use for a design can be intimidating, but it doesn't have to be! Some basic understanding of color theory will go a long way toward making you feel more comfortable about choosing colors. Ultimately, though, it's good to remember that there is no right way or wrong way to color a design in this book, so don't be afraid to dive in!

It all starts with the primary colors red, yellow, and blue. These three colors can be mixed to create a whole rainbow, but they cannot be created by mixing other colors—this is why they are "primary." If you mix two primary colors, you will get the secondary colors orange (red + yellow), green (yellow + blue), and purple (blue + red). Mixing a primary color and a secondary color will result in a tertiary color. These include orange-yellow, yellow-green, green-blue, blue-purple, red-purple, and orange-red. Any primary, secondary, or tertiary color can be darkened or lightened by the addition of white or black. The result is a tint or shade of the original color. For example, pink is a tint of red created by adding white, and burgundy is a shade of red created by adding black.

Take a look at the color wheel. It is your most helpful tool when it comes to understanding how colors relate to one another. Think of the color wheel as having two sides. On one side are the warm colors yellow, orange, and red. On the other side are the cool colors green, blue, and purple. Warm colors are bold and invoke excitement. They will pop out of your design, especially when paired with cool colors. Cool colors are calm and invoke relaxation and peacefulness. They will recede in a design. Warm colors will always pair well with one another and cool colors will always pair well with one another.

Another handy color relationship you should be aware of is analogous colors. Analogous colors are next to one another on the color wheel. One reason warm colors and cool colors go well together is because they are analogous, but you don't have to limit yourself to warm and cool colors only. A mix of warm and cool analogous colors will make a great color scheme. For example, blue and green (both cool) pair well with yellow (warm).

One final color relationship for your arsenal is complementary colors. Complementary colors are directly opposite one another on the color wheel. If you look at the color wheel, you'll see that all complementary pairings contain a warm and a cool color. For example, orange (warm) and blue (cool). As their name suggests, complementary colors "complement" one another. They also stand out against one another more than they do against any other color. You can use this relationship to create some real impact!

Warm colors

Cool colors

Analogous

Complementary

TIPS AND TRICKS FOR CHALKBOARD ART

The black chalkboard background used for these pieces adds another element to consider when coloring. Here are some tips and tricks that you might find helpful. Also be sure to check out the colored designs on the following pages for inspiration.

Keep it light and bright. Remember that you're working on a black background. This means the colors that will be the most visible are bright ones, like warm colors and neons. If you prefer a cool color palette, try using lighter pastel shades of your favorite colors, like light blue and green, instead of dark shades like navy and forest green.

Add to the background. Just because the background is black doesn't mean you can't add to it. Use light-colored pencils and gel pens to add your own lettering, flourishes, and patterning to the existing designs. Gel pens can even be used to apply additional detail to an area that's been colored with markers or colored pencils.

Lay it on thick. You can give your piece lots of dimension by layering colors and adding shading. This will make the color elements of your design stand out even more against the simple, dark background.

Let it be. White lettering on a black background is THE classic chalk look. If you like that simple style, consider leaving the letters in a design white and coloring everything else. Or, for a modern twist, color the letters, too!

Rough it up. It might be tempting to smooth out your coloring to avoid texture and imperfections, but these look perfectly natural in a chalk piece. Embrace the texture your colored pencils create or the lines you might get from overlapping your markers. These imperfections will add character to your piece and make it unique.

If you love the classic chalkboard look, be sure to leave plenty of areas in your design white.

Don't be afraid of texture! It pairs beautifully with chalkboard art. Look at the texture created on the flowers in this design.

COLOR
INSPIRATION

It's so much fun to color a new piece of art and share it with others. The following pages are filled with colored examples from this book to get you thinking about and imagining all of the things you can do with the designs. As you look at them, take mental note of the color schemes that make you smile. I hope these pieces inspire you before you sit down to color your own beautiful art in your unique style.

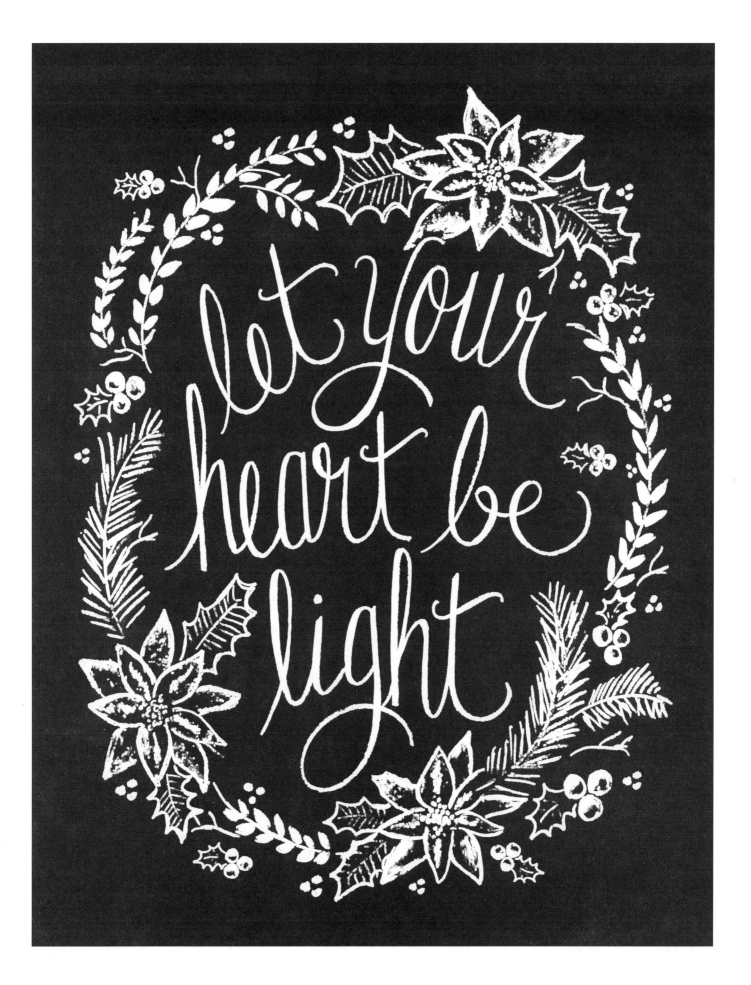

May Christmas lend a special charm
To all you chance to do.
And may the season light your way
To hopes and dreams anew.

—Garnett Ann Schultz, My Christmas Wish

When it snows, you have two choices:
shovel or make snow angels.

–Unknown

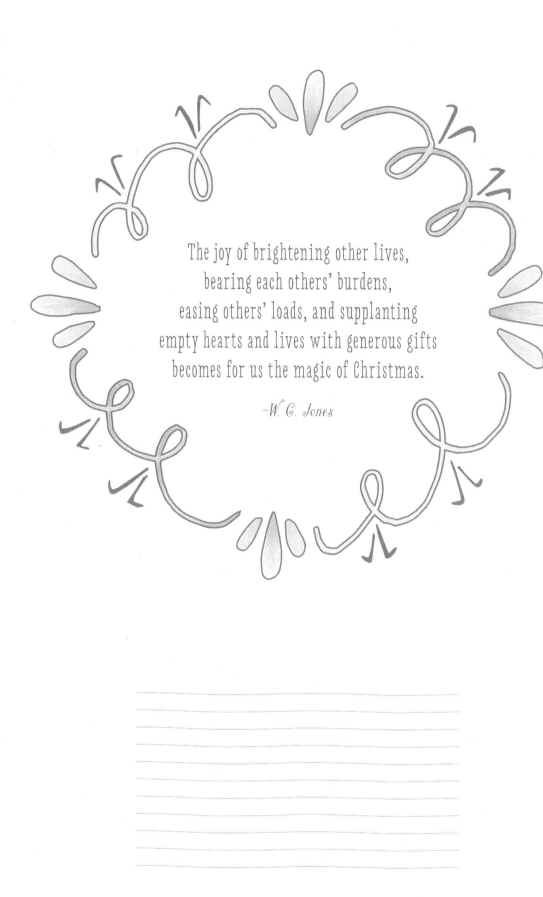

The joy of brightening other lives,
bearing each others' burdens,
easing others' loads, and supplanting
empty hearts and lives with generous gifts
becomes for us the magic of Christmas.

–W. C. Jones

It's the most wonderful time of the year
There'll be much mistletoeing
And hearts will be glowing
When loved ones are near
It's the most wonderful time of the year

*—Edward Pola and George Wyle,
It's the Most Wonderful Time of the Year*

I think Christmas is about celebration and come on, on the inside everyone wants to dance.

–Unknown

Believe in what your heart is saying,
Hear the melody that's playing.
There's no time to waste,
There's so much to celebrate.
Believe in what you feel inside,
And give your dreams the wings to fly.
You have everything you need,
if you just believe.

—Josh Groban, Believe

There is nothing in the world so irresistibly
contagious as laughter and good humor.

—Charles Dickens, A Christmas Carol

It's all fun and games 'til
Santa checks the naughty list.

–Unknown

Play with traditional Christmas colors by using different shades of red and green, like the green and pink used in this design.

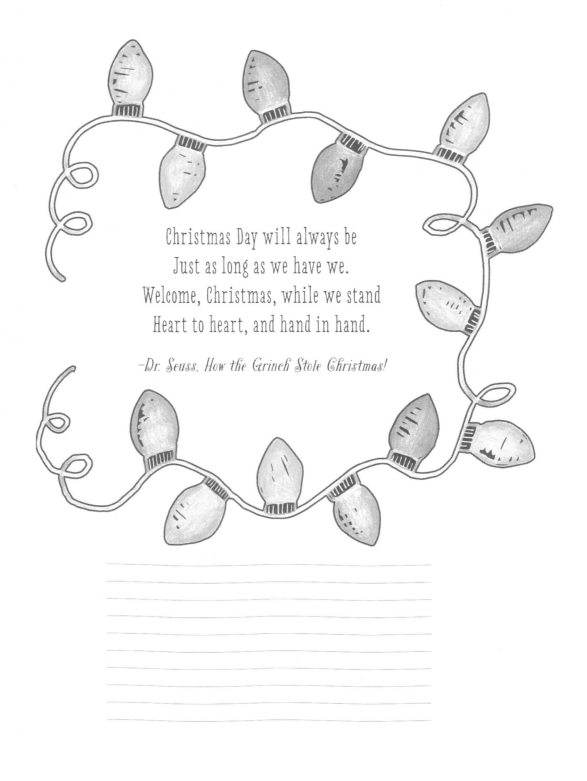

Christmas Day will always be
Just as long as we have we.
Welcome, Christmas, while we stand
Heart to heart, and hand in hand.

—Dr. Seuss, How the Grinch Stole Christmas!

Use the traditional colors of the season to infuse your art with Christmas spirit. Try gold for a really special effect.

The best and most beautiful things in
the world cannot be seen or even touched.
They must be felt with the heart.

–Helen Keller

Have fun filling this design with bright colors like the lights around your house at the holiday season.

Seeing isn't believing. Believing is seeing.

—The Santa Clause

You don't need loads of colors to create a beautiful design. This image uses a few simple shades with great results—and remember to leave some areas white!

A balanced diet is a
Christmas cookie in each hand.

–Unknown

_____

_____

_____

_____

_____

_____

_____

_____

_____

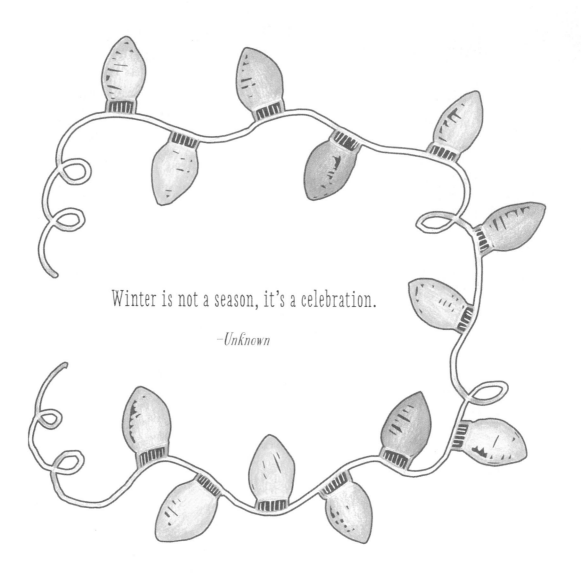

Winter is not a season, it's a celebration.

–Unknown

_____

_____

_____

_____

_____

_____

_____

_____

_____

_____

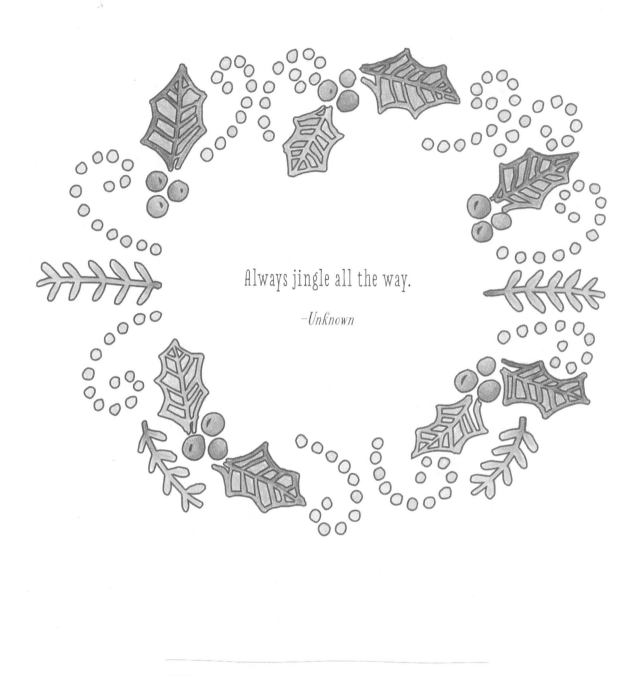

Always jingle all the way.

–Unknown

Just remember, the true spirit of
Christmas lies in your heart.

-The Polar Express

He's making a list and checking it twice;
Gonna find out who's naughty and nice
Santa Claus is comin' to town

–Santa Claus Is Comin' to Town

Winter came down to our home one night,
quietly pirouetting in on silvery-toed slippers
of snow, and we, we were children once again.

–Bill Morgan, Jr.

I will honor Christmas in my heart & try to keep it all the year

— Charles Dickens

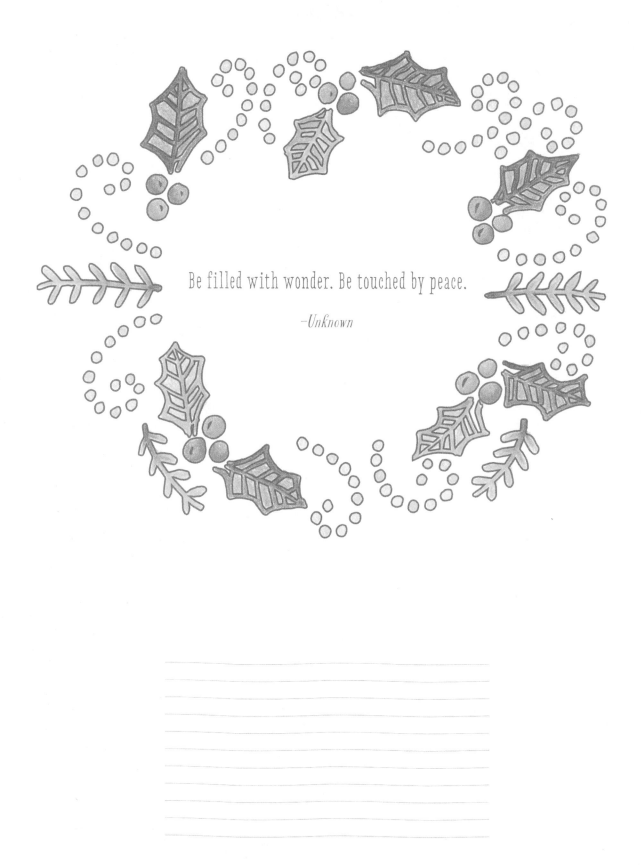

Be filled with wonder. Be touched by peace.

—Unknown

_____

_____

_____

_____

_____

_____

_____

_____

_____

What happens under the mistletoe
stays under the mistletoe.

–Unknown

_____

_____

_____

_____

_____

_____

_____

_____

Christmas, my child, is love in action.
Every time we love, every time we give,
it's Christmas.

—Dale Evans

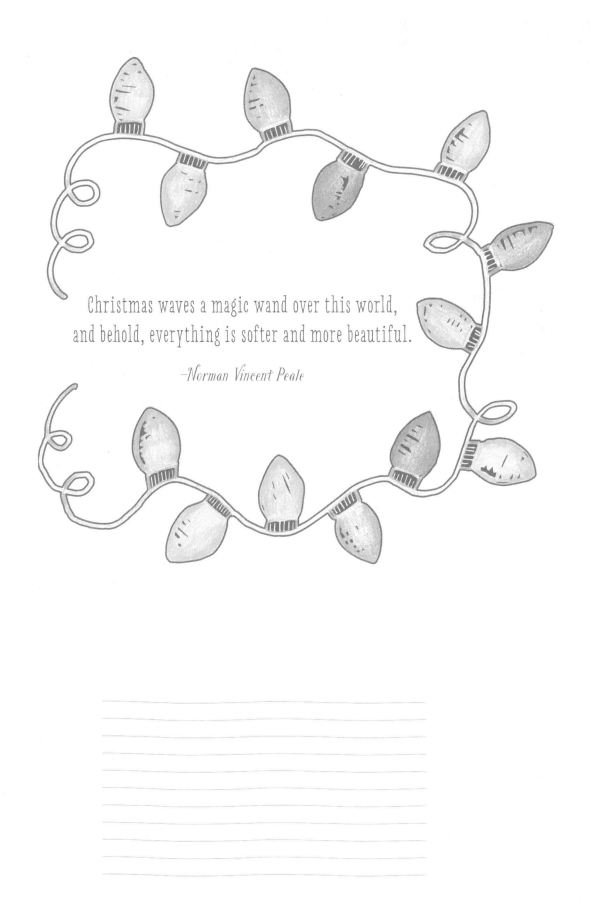

Christmas waves a magic wand over this world,
and behold, everything is softer and more beautiful.

–Norman Vincent Peale

I'm dreaming of a white Christmas.
But if the white runs out
I'll drink the red.

—Unknown

_____

_____

_____

_____

_____

_____

_____

_____

The best of all gifts around any Christmas tree:
the presence of a happy family all
wrapped up in each other.

—Unknown

_____
_____
_____
_____
_____
_____
_____
_____
_____

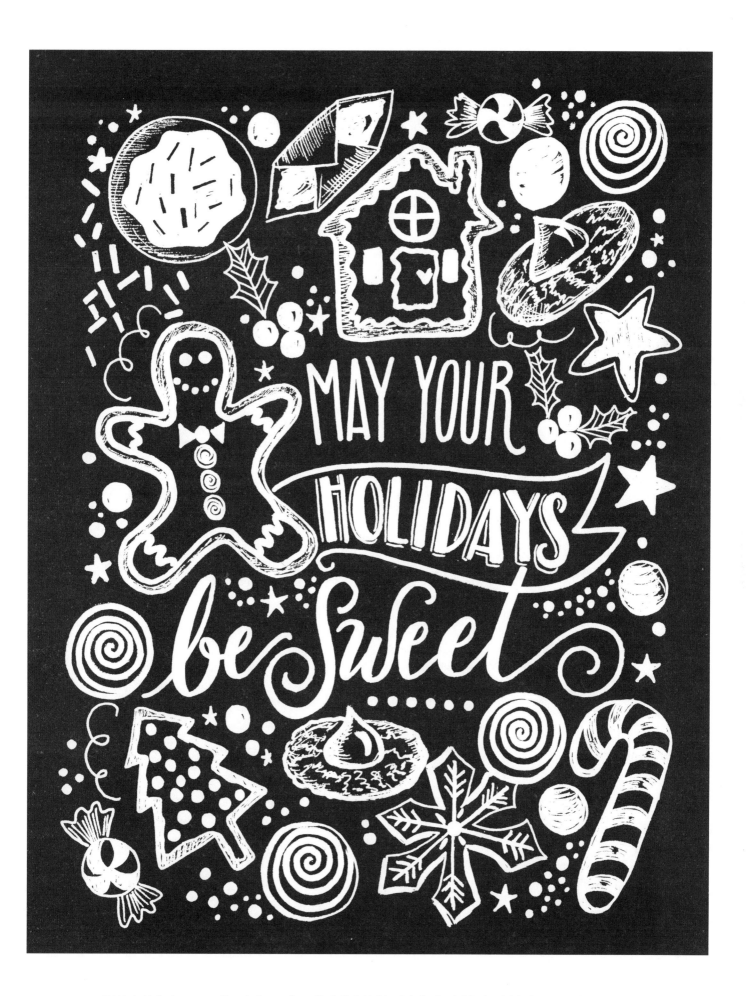

Today's Christmas should mean
creating happy hours for tomorrow
and reliving those of yesterday.

–Gladys Taber

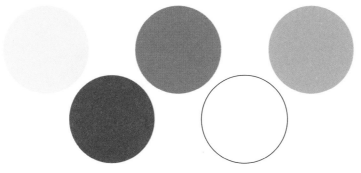

The color palette for this design is inspired by the cool wintry colors of snow and ice.

Some people are worth melting for.

−Olaf, Frozen

_____
_____
_____
_____
_____
_____
_____
_____
_____
_____

Take inspiration from the world around you when choosing colors. Make this Christmas tree green and fill it with bright-colored ornaments.

It's not what's under the Christmas tree
that matters. It's who's around it.

–Unknown

_____
_____
_____
_____
_____
_____
_____
_____
_____

This piece is fun and festive. Pair it with colors that match, then frame it and use it to deck your halls!

The best way to spread Christmas cheer
is singing loud for all to hear!

-Elf

_____

_____

_____

_____

_____

_____

_____

_____

_____

_____

Complementary colors like the yellow and purple used for the center stocking will always stand out against one another. Use them for bold contrast.

Winter is the time for comfort, for good
food and warmth, for the touch of a
friendly hand and for a talk beside
the fire: it is the time for home.

—Edith Sitwell

Gifts of time and love are surely the basic
ingredients of a truly merry Christmas.

—Peg Bracken

_____

_____

_____

_____

_____

_____

_____

_____

_____

_____

_____

The greatest good is what
we do for one another.

—Unknown

WARM WISHES & PEPPERMINT KISSES

At Christmas play and make good cheer,
for Christmas comes but once a year.

–Thomas Tusser

Our hearts grow tender with childhood memories and love of kindred, and we are better throughout the year for having, in spirit, become a child again at Christmas-time.

–Laura Ingalls Wilder